Esca... ...n the City

Contents

Titles in the Runway series

Badger Publishing Limited
Oldmedow Road,
Hardwick Industrial Estate,
King's Lynn PE30 4JJ
Telephone: 01438 791037
www.badgerlearning.co.uk

Escape from the City ISBN 978 1 84691 373 0

Publisher: David Jamieson
Commissioning Editor: Carrie Lewis
Design: Fiona Grant
Illustration: Oliver Lake, Aleksandar Sotirovski, Enzo Troiano

Escape from the City

Written by Alison Hawes
Illustrated by Oliver Lake

Badger LEARNING

A sickness was in the city.
People were dying.
My family died from the sickness.
I didn't want to die, so I ran away.

I came to a village.
The people said, "Go away!
We don't want the sickness here!"

I came to another village.
The people said, "Go away!
We don't want the sickness here!"

No one in the villages helped me.
So I stole some food and ran away.

At last, I came to my uncle's village.
I wanted him to help me.

My uncle said,
"I want to help you, but I can't."

My aunt said, "We must help him!"
She burned my clothes.
"No one will get sick if we do this." She said.

I will not go back to the city.
My family is here, now.

>>The Scarf Sling

Written by Alison Milford
Illustrated by Aleksandar Sotirovski

Ben and his friends were in the park.
Ben saw a girl on a bike.
Another bike hit her and sped away.

"Are you OK?" asked Ben.
"My arm is hurt," said the girl.

Ben put his scarf around the girl's arm.
"Hurry up Ben," said his friends.

"That girl was hurt," said Ben. "Who was she?" asked Ben's friends. But the girl had vanished.

The next day, Ben and his mum were in the car.
Another car hit them and speeded away.

Nearby was a travellers' caravan site.
A man and a girl came out of a caravan.

"Are you OK?" asked the girl.
"My arm is hurt," said Ben.

"Put this scarf around it," said the girl.
"A kind stranger gave it to me yesterday."

An Act of Kindness

Written by Alison Milford
Illustrated by Enzo Troiano

Every morning some school children were on the bus.
Every morning an old man was on the bus.

The children thought the old man was horrible.
The old man thought the children were rude.

One morning the old man wasn't on the bus.
The children were very happy and very loud!

The next morning, the old man still wasn't
on the bus.
The children were worried.

They knocked on the old man's door.
They looked through the window.

They looked through the letterbox.
They saw the old man on the floor.

The school children called 999.
They asked for an ambulance to come
quickly.

The paramedics knew the old man.
He visited people at the hospital.

>>> Vocabulary ___

Escape from the City

escape
sickness
family
city
people
dying/died
village
stole
burned

The Scarf Sling

scarf
sling
hurt
speeded
vanished
travellers
caravan
kind
stranger

An Act of Kindness

thought
horrible
rude
worried
knocked
letterbox
ambulance
paramedics

>>> Story questions

Escape from the City

Why were people in the city dying?
How did the storyteller find things to eat?
How did burning the clothes stop people getting sick?

The Scarf Sling

What happened to the girl in the park?
Why do you think she vanished afterwards?
Do you think the girl at the end remembers the boy from the park?

An Act of Kindness

Why were the children pleased that the man wasn't on the bus?
How did they know that something was wrong?
Why do you think old people and children might not like each other?